The Swimsuit Lesson

Jon Holsten

illustrations by Scott Freeman

BOOKS

THE SWIMSUIT LESSON
Second Edition

Holsten Books, P.O. Box 772, Fort Collins CO 80522

Visit our Web site: www.holstenbooks.com

Art Director and Book Designer: Ray Tollison
Editor: Christy Fagerlin

Scott Freeman was born and raised in the suburbs of St. Louis. Displaying unique giftedness from childhood, Scott attended Kansas City Art Institute, in Kansas City, Missouri, where he earned a Fine Art Degree in 1982. His varied career includes 2 years teaching at a small, private school; 3 years as a designer and glass painter at a stained glass studio in Kansas City; 3 years running his own illustration studio; and nearly 10 years at Hallmark Cards, Inc. in Kansas City, working as an artist/designer. Scott, and his wife Mollie, have five children, and make their home in Loveland, Colorado.

Visit Scott online at: www.freemanartgallery.com

Library of Congress Catalog-in-Publication Data

Holsten, Jon
    The Swimsuit Lesson/by Jon Holsten; illustrations by Scott Freeman
         p.   cm.
    Summary: Mark and Lisa's summertime fun turns into a valuable lesson every child should learn.

      ISBN-13: 978-0-9769730-1-0
      ISBN-10: 0-9769730-1-4

Library of Congress Control Number: 2006922927

Printed in the United States of America.

For Every Child
and Those Who Teach Them

"It's a great day to play in the sprinkler!" says Lisa.

The sun is shining, but Mark shivers.

"I'm cold!" exclaims Mark – his teeth chattering.

"Kids! Come take a break," Mom shouts. "You've been outside a long time!"

Mark and Lisa dry off from head to toe
and run inside the house.

Mom pours the kids a glass of lemonade.

"While you rest, I have something
very important to tell you," says Mom.

"You're both getting older now, and sometimes you will be away from Mom and Dad.

"When you're not with us, most people will treat you nicely. But some people will not."

"What do you mean?" asks Mark.

Mom looks kindly at the children.

"Mark and Lisa," Mom says. "Some people may try to touch little boys or girls on parts of their body where they shouldn't touch them. That's wrong."

"I don't understand," says Lisa.

"You're wearing your swimsuits," says Mom. "This is a good time to explain what I mean."

"Your body is very special. Every part is good, but some parts of your body are private."

"Like my bottom?" asks Mark.

"Yes," replies Mom, "like your bottom."

"Your swimsuits cover those special parts of your body that I'm talking about."

"Listen closely," says Mom.

"I love you. I want you to be safe."

"If anyone ever touches you, or even tries to touch you on your private parts – you must tell Mom or Dad. Even if the person tells you not to say anything."

"Will we get in trouble if we tell you?"
asks Lisa.

"No, sweetheart," explains Mom. "You will not get in trouble. Mom and Dad will be proud of you for telling us. And we will help the person who touched you understand it is wrong."

"What if I'm afraid to tell you?" inquires Mark.

"I would understand if you were scared," Mom says, "but I am asking you to tell me even when you're afraid. You will feel better if you tell me things like that."

"What about kids who don't have parents?" Lisa wonders. "Who do they tell?"

"That's a good question," answers Mom. "They should tell a grown-up they trust – like a teacher."

Mom asks Mark and Lisa if they have any more questions.

The kids think.

... And think

... And think.

"I do!" exclaims Mark.

"Can we go play in the sprinkler again?"

Everyone laughs.

Mark and Lisa run and jump in the water.

They are happy Mom loves them enough to help them be safe.

The Swimsuit Lesson
a parent's guide

by Jon Holsten

Why This Book is Important

You've heard it said, "Ignorance is bliss." When it comes to sexual abuse on children – nothing could be further from the truth. The only person who benefits from ignorance is the perpetrator. Everyone else lives in either false security waiting to be victimized, or in the dark world of anger, fear, and pain experienced by those children and families who fall prey.

Sexual abuse of children is a very real problem. Many of you reading this guide were victimized as children. If you are not a victim, you can be certain one is nearby. It is a travesty that many parents choose to avoid the issue – for by doing so, they unwittingly place their children in harm's potential path. Some parents are simply out of touch with reality – thinking that child molestation is rare – that it happens only in certain circles, certain type neighborhoods or certain socioeconomic populations. The fact is it happens in every circle – in every type neighborhood – amongst every socioeconomic population. It is time for parents and guardians of children to recognize child sexual abuse as the sick epidemic it is.

The U.S. Department of Justice reports that 67% of all sexual assault victims are children. Another study by the National Center for Victims of Crime (2000) shows 33% of girls (1 out of 3) are sexually abused before the age of 18. Sixteen percent of boys (roughly 1 out of 6) are sexually abused before the age of 18. We would all like to think our children are immune. They are not.

Most parents forbid their children to play with matches because the ensuing result is obvious. We take time to explain to our children the danger of fire and expect other parents to do the same. Should we not, then, work diligently to keep our children out of those unseen risky situations and teach them what to do if someone exploits them sexually?

The Swimsuit Lesson is written for two reasons. First, to help parents explain to their children what is appropriate and what is inappropriate as it relates to physical contact with other people. Second, the story helps children understand what to do if someone takes advantage of them sexually. In other words – we want to use parental and guardian influence to reduce the incidents of child sexual abuse, and encourage healing disclosure when the unthinkable happens. It is a parent's responsibility to guide their children through this process.

How Sexual Offenders Operate

It is important to understand, in part, how sexual offenders identify the children they victimize. It is impossible to list all of the strategies used. Perversion does not lack creativity; therefore, caution above and beyond what is recommended here must be exercised.

The person *most likely* to sexually abuse your child is not an odd-looking fellow dressed in a trench coat and lurking in the park. While that scenario is certainly possible, the more valid concern is a person your child knows – and trusts. The sex offender looks for a child who trusts him, and can be convinced to stay quiet about inappropriate physical contact. It could be anyone around you: a relative, a neighbor, a friend's family member, or your babysitter. I realize this information casts suspicion on most everyone, but the reality is, many children are victimized by the last person a parent would suspect. That said, my goal is not to sow unreasonable fear, or paranoia. Obviously, not every person who expresses interest in your child is a sex offender, nor should they be treated as such. Instead, you as a parent simply need to stay alert to anything unusual in your child's relationships. In addition, your child must be equipped with knowledge of what is appropriate and charged to disclose suspicious behavior.

Some Suggestions When Using This Book

Discussing sexuality and/or sexual abuse with your child can be uncomfortable. Many of us were raised in homes where conversation about such things was non-existent. In today's world we cannot afford to skirt the issue. That is why we provide this resource. It is a simple, yet effective way to open dialogue and communicate truth to your child.

There are many ways to introduce this book to your child. I suggest you set aside specific time to go through the story. ***Try to schedule a block of time when you are least likely to be interrupted***. If you have multiple children – a group reading may reduce anxiety for everyone involved, and spark great conversation. ***Make sure you read the whole story prior to sharing it with your child***. You will be better prepared to address any questions your child has. It will also give you a chance to identify parts of the story you want to stress to your child.

The story involves Mark and Lisa, two young children dressed in swimsuits and playing in the sprinkler. ***To bring the story alive, you may consider having your kids dress in their own swimsuits***.

When the mother in the story explains that Mark and Lisa's swimsuits cover those special parts of their body which are private, your children will better relate with the information provided. **You can take the time to make sure your child understands exactly what parts of his or her body are off-limits to others.** Be careful not to communicate a negative view of their private body parts, but rather stress the special nature of their bodies. Depending on how open your family is with such information, **this is also a great time to communicate anatomically correct names for their body parts.** Regardless of your comfort level, **make sure your child understands the specific parts of his or her body that are not to be touched. For a girl, this will be (at a minimum) her vagina, buttocks, and breasts. For the boy (at a minimum), his penis and buttocks.** If you are more comfortable communicating this issue with your child in private, then head that direction. **The main thing is that you cover the information.**

On page 22, the mother in the story explains to the children the importance of disclosing any time someone has contact with their private parts. **Obviously, there will be times when a parent, guardian, or physician has legitimate contact with a child's private parts. Any such contact is a case by case situation that can be explained as appropriate when that information is brought to the parent.** There is no harm in your child disclosing that information. The important thing is to catch any illegitimate contact.

In that same portion of the conversation Mom exhorts the children to disclose inappropriate touching "even if the person tells you not to." This is a critical piece of information your child needs to understand. Some child molesters demand the victim keep quiet about the contact – going as far as to threaten to hurt or kill a family member. They may tell the child that his parents will be upset or disappointed with him. **There is a lot of psychology behind these threats, but the important thing is for your child to know that you are in his corner.**

Let him know you understand such threats may be made, and that you want him to tell you – even if he is scared about what may happen. I explain to my children that such people are just scared to get in trouble and will say anything to avoid telling the truth.

At one point in the story, Lisa asks if she and her brother would get in trouble if someone touched them inappropriately. Mother reassures Lisa that they will not get in trouble and that Mom and Dad "will be proud of you for telling us." *Use this opportunity to dispel your child's fear that Mom and Dad will be angry with her, or that punishment quickly follows disclosure. This is also a good time to remind children of their need to be honest in all situations – and your expectation that they never say they were touched when they weren't.*

As the story draws to an end, Mom asks the kids if they have any questions. While Mark is more interested in getting back to the sprinkler, your child may want to talk about the story. Take the time to process what they've learned and answer any questions. Don't be surprised, however, if your child jumps to the next activity just like Mark. When introduced in a low-key, non-threatening manner, your child may well take the lesson to heart and move on.

I recommend reading The Swimsuit Lesson several times with your child, until you feel confident she understands the information, and is able to voice her plan to tell you if anything inappropriate happens. Some parents may choose to remove the parent's guide from the story book, and make it part of the child's everyday library. Simply having the book around will serve as a valuable reminder for your child.

What to Do if Your Child Discloses Sexual Abuse

Simply reading *The Swimsuit Lesson* could encourage children to come forward with information of inappropriate touching. If this happens, try to avoid a highly emotional response in front of your child, and move to a location where you can speak with the child privately. Avoid asking a lot of questions. Instead, let the child simply talk about the incident. Thank your child for telling you about the incident(s), let him know he is not in trouble, that you are proud of him, and that he did nothing wrong. If the story is detailed, or includes sexual information your child should not yet know, keep your distance from the possible suspect, and immediately report the allegation to local law enforcement.

Parents and guardians are often hesitant to report sexual abuse to law enforcement, especially if a family member is involved. Failing to report such abuse is dangerous – even if the alleged suspect denies it ever happened, or claims it "only happened once." Individuals who sexually abuse children need severe consequences and intensive sexual offender treatment. Countless well-meaning parents have agreed to by-pass law enforcement – thus allowing the perpetrator

to victimize even more children. Child sexual abusers cannot just flip a switch and stop their behavior. For the sake of everyone involved – especially the children – it is imperative that trained investigators look into credible allegations.